Disney LEARNING

Reading, Writing, and Math

GRADE **1**

NELSON

This workbook belongs to:

_____

Disney LEARNING

COPYRIGHT © 2018 Disney Enterprises, Inc.
All rights reserved.

Published by Nelson Education Ltd.

ISBN-13: 978-0-17-689226-5
ISBN-10: 0-17-689226-5

Printed and bound in Canada
1 2 3 4   22 21 20 19

For more information contact Nelson Education Ltd.,
1120 Birchmount Road, Toronto, Ontario M1K 5G4.
Or you can visit our website at nelson.com.

Credits: 69: © Nelson Education Ltd. 103: (dates) picturepartners/
Shutterstock.com; (blue plates) Borna_Mirahmadian/Shutterstock.com.
107: (left to right) Rido/Shutterstock.com; Africa Studio/Shutterstock.com;
volkovslava/Shutterstock.com; MarcusVDT/Shutterstock.com; Dorottya
Mathe/Shutterstock.com; 5 second Studio/Shutterstock.com; pathdoc/
Shutterstock.com; volkovslava/Shutterstock.com. 122: (money) © 2017
Royal Canadian Mint. All rights reserved. 151: (toothpaste) F16-ISO100/
Shutterstock.com; (paper clips) escova/Shutterstock.com; (comb)
terekhov igor/Shutterstock.com. 157: (left to right) AlenKadr/Shutterstock
.com; DW labs Incorporated/Shutterstock.com; Andrey_Kuzmin/
Shutterstock.com; Daria Medvedeva/Shutterstock.com; topnatthapon/
Shutterstock.com; Big Pants Production/Shutterstock.com. 182: (paint
cans) Brooke Becker/Shutterstock.com; (wool) Picsfive/Shutterstock.com;
(baskets) Gong To/Shutterstock.com. 183: (boxes) jocic/Shutterstock.com.
186: (orange wool) Simon Mayer/Shutterstock.com; (green wool) Vasilius/
Shutterstock.com; (blue wool) Nataliia K/Shutterstock.com.

Contents

Ready to Read and Write

Ready for Math

What Is Your Name?

This is Elsa.

Elsa is her name.

Print your name.

Draw a picture of yourself.

Print your name below your picture.

Your child may need help spelling or printing their first and last name. Help your child add an "I can ..." sentence to their picture (I can dance; I can read).

Let's Create a Wintry Alphabet

Elsa fills the castle with snow for Anna.

Fill in the missing letters.

A B __ D E __ G H I __ K L M N

__ P Q __ S T U __ W X __ Z

Fill in the missing letters.

a b c __ e f __ h i __ k l __ __ n

o __ q r __ t u __ __ w __ y __

Learn Together
Provide opportunities for your child to learn **alphabetical order**. Cover up a letter and ask, "What letter is missing?" Name a letter and ask, "Which letter comes after this one? Which letter comes before it?" Take turns with your child.

A, B, C, and D

Trace and print the letters.

A A A A A

a a a a a

B B B B B

b b b b b

C C C C C

c c c c c

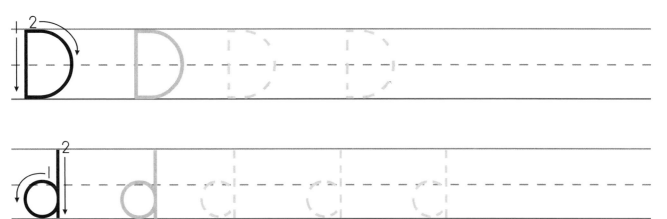

Trace the uppercase letters in red.

Trace the lowercase letters in blue.

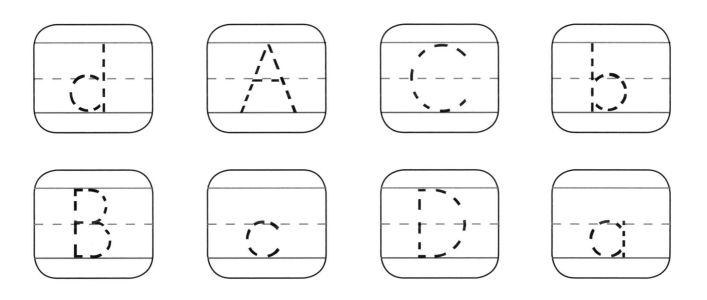

Learn Together Ask your child to name each letter out loud. Use your finger to trace the letters **a**, **b**, **c**, and **d** on your child's hand. Can they identify the letters as uppercase or lowercase letters?

9

E, F, G, and H

Trace and print the letters.

E

e

F

f

G

g

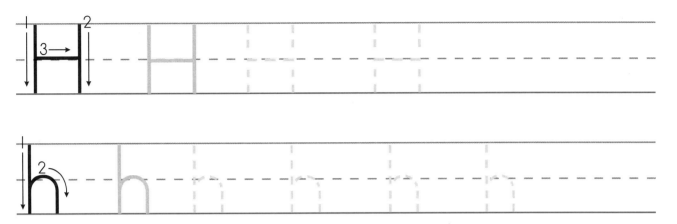

Trace the uppercase letters in red.

Trace the lowercase letters in blue.

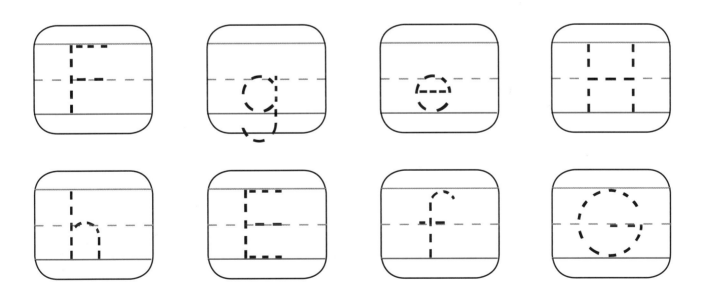

Learn Together

Ask your child to name each letter out loud. Use your finger to trace the letters **e**, **f**, **g**, and **h** on your child's hand. Can they identify the letters as uppercase or lowercase letters?

I, J, K, and L

Trace and print the letters.

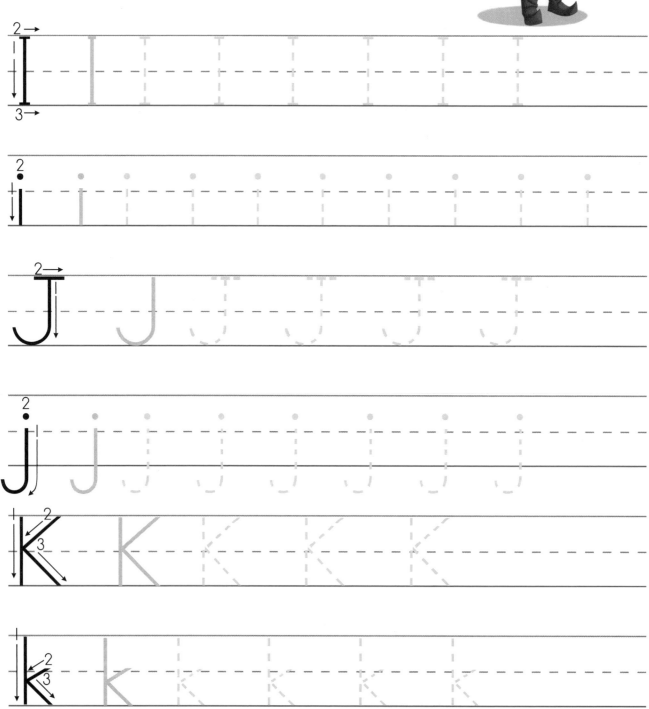

Trace the uppercase letters in red.

Trace the lowercase letters in blue.

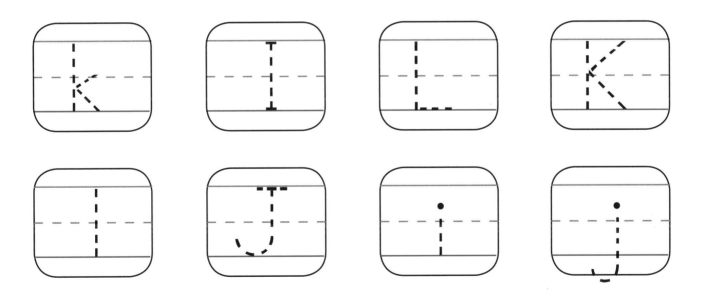

M, N, O, and P

Trace and print the letters.

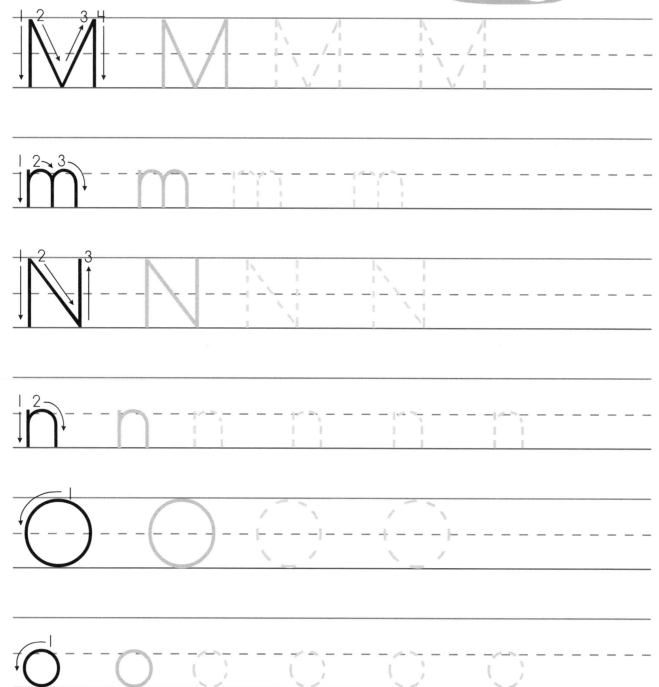

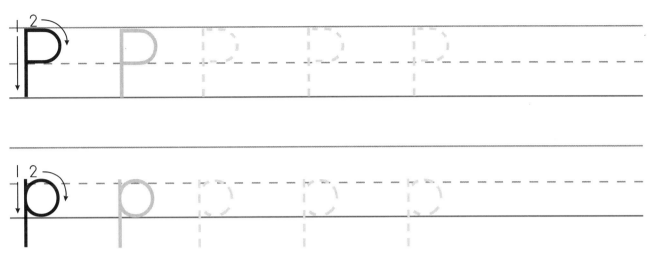

Trace the uppercase letters in red.

Trace the lowercase letters in blue.

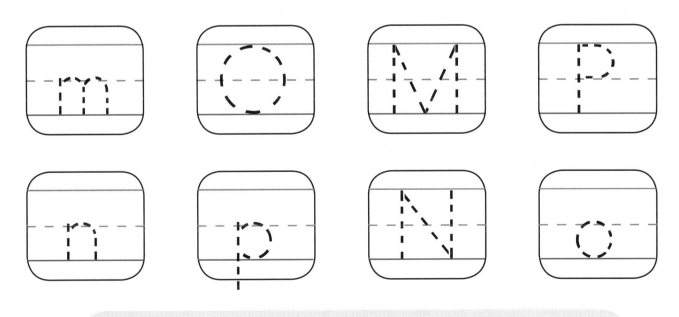

Q, R, S, and T

Trace and print the letters.

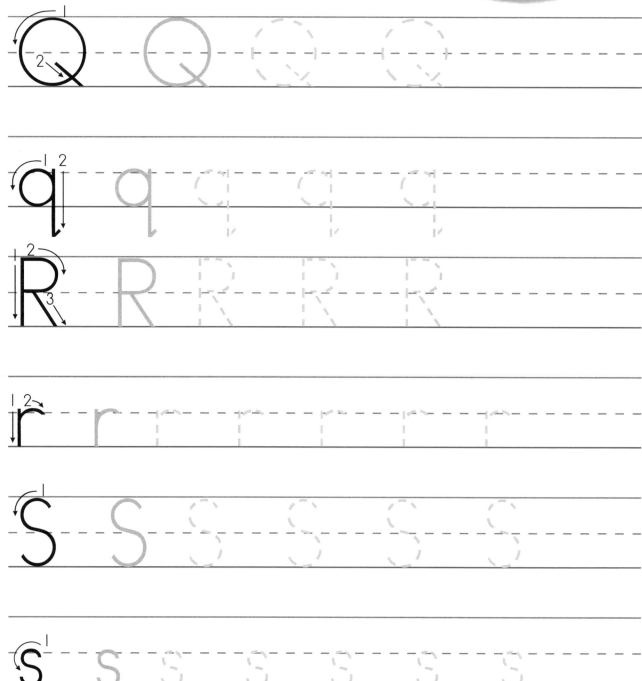

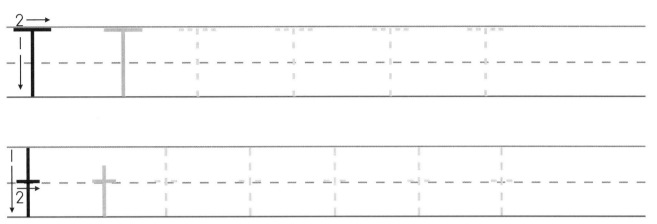

Trace the uppercase letters in red.

Trace the lowercase letters in blue.

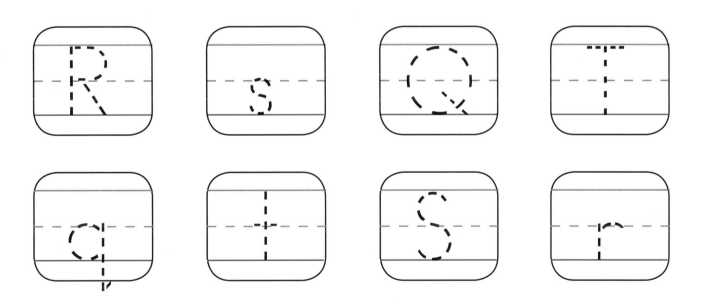

Learn Together

Ask your child to name each letter out loud. Use your finger to trace the letters **q**, **r**, **s**, and **t** on your child's hand. Can they identify the letters as uppercase or lowercase letters?

U, V, W, and X

Trace and print the letters.

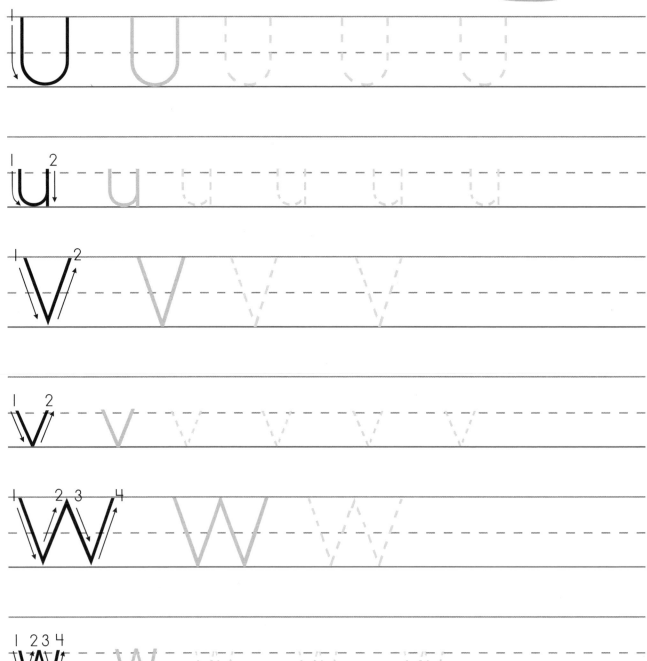

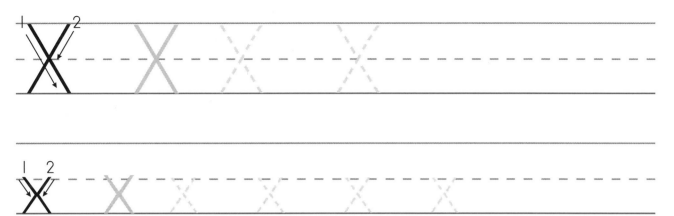

Trace the uppercase letters in red.

Trace the lowercase letters in blue.

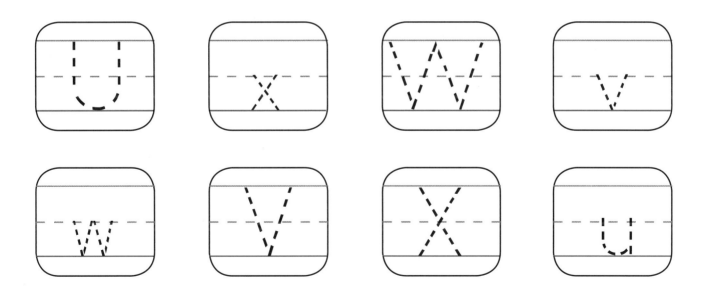

Learn Together

Ask your child to name each letter out loud. Use your finger to trace the letters **u**, **v**, **w**, and **x** on your child's hand. Can they identify the letters as uppercase or lowercase letters?

Y and Z

Trace and print the letters.

Trace the uppercase letters in red.

Trace the lowercase letters in blue.

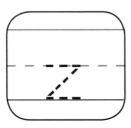 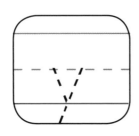 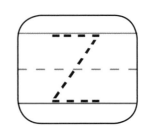 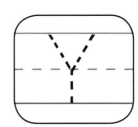

Elsa wants to protect her sister.
Trace the letters.

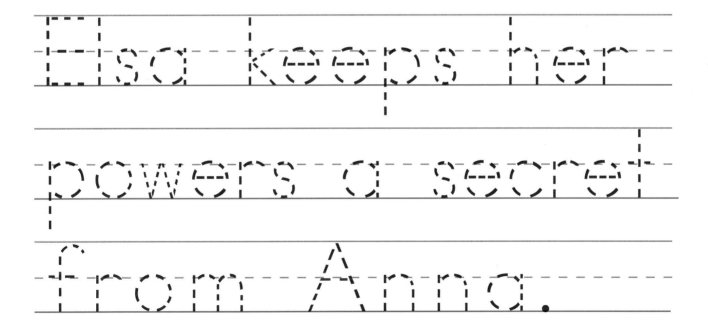

Elsa keeps her powers a secret from Anna.

Learn Together Sing the alphabet song with you child. Pause now and then for your child to supply the next letter.

21

Let's Make Words

These words are all part of the

ay word family.

Trace the first letter.

Say each word out loud.

hay   day   way   play

These words are all part of the **an** word family

Trace the first letter.

Say each word out loud.

can   pan   ran   man

Anna wants to play with Elsa. Trace the missing letters.

Can you come to

build a snowman?

Let's go play!

Words I Know

There are some words you will read often.
We call those words **popcorn words**.

Read these popcorn words out loud.

he   they   her
     she   him
                                 them

Fill in the missing popcorn words.

Today is Elsa's coronation. ___ ___ ___ is nervous to open the castle gates.

Anna is excited to have guests in the castle! She can not wait to meet ___ ___ ___ ___ .

Learn Together

Help your child read the popcorn or **sight words**, noting the letters they begin with and how long each word is. Your child can circle any other words they already know in the sentences.

More Words I Know

Hans does not **see** Anna when he runs into **her**.

He stops to **help** Anna get back up. Hans is very

polite. **He** makes Anna smile.

Read these popcorn words out loud.

he   her   help

     look   see   very

<u>Underline</u> the popcorn words below.

Anna is excited to see all of Arendelle.

Anna wants to look at the whole town!

She meets Hans. He makes her smile.

Anna is very happy!

Learn Together
Help your child read each sentence, pausing at each sight word to let them read it. Make flash cards with some of the sight words (see the list in the glossary). Ask your child to read the words and use them in sentences.

I Am Ready to Read!

Anna stands **with** Elsa at the coronation.

The coronation is **very** important **because** Elsa will become queen.

Read these popcorn words out loud.

because   **with**   **that**

very   **some**

Fill in the missing popcorn words.

All the people are ___ ___ ___ ___ excited to see

Elsa, ___ ___ ___ ___ ___ ___ ___ they have never
seen their queen.

Anna eats ___ ___ ___ ___ chocolate at the party.

I Am Reading!

Hans **is** very sweet to Anna.

Anna wonders if he **will be** her true love.

Anna and Hans **are** getting along.

Hans asks Anna if he **can** marry her!

Read these popcorn words out loud.

is   **will**   **are**

can   **be**

Fill in the missing popcorn words.

Anna asks Elsa if she ___ ___ ___ marry Hans.

Elsa ___ ___ ___ ___ not allow it.

Anna ___ ___ upset with Elsa!

Learn Together

On a blank piece of paper, create a large word bank with the sight words your child knows. With your child, write a note to a friend, using some of these words.

Fun with Opposites

Opposites are words that mean completely different things.

Anna is **loud**.

Elsa is **quiet**.

Loud is the opposite of _____.

Elsa is the **older** sister.

Anna is the **younger** sister.

Younger is the opposite of _____.

Even sisters can be opposites.

Match each word to its opposite.

old   bad

slow   hot

good   new

tall   short

cold   fast

Learn Together Use these or other opposites to create sentences. Your child can fill in the missing word. (Anna is very loud, not very _____.)

33

Opposite Actions

Anna and Elsa are **sitting**.

Kristoff is **standing**.

Act out these opposites.

sit
stand

asleep
awake

smile
frown

close
open

Match each word to its opposite.

right   night

day   out

in   wrong

dark   dirty

clean   light

Learn Together Take turns acting out opposites and trying to guess them (asleep/awake, open/close, shout/whisper, float/sink).

Rhyme Time

Rhyming words have letters at the end
that sound the same.

(Circle) the words that rhyme.

ice   nice   dice   snow   glow   blow

cold   gold   old

Say the words out loud. Listen to the rhyme.

(Circle) the words that rhyme.

Anna and Hans want to marry with Elsa's permission.
"No" is Elsa's final decision.

Elsa tells Anna, "It's not true love."
Anna is upset and accidentally removes Elsa's glove.

Elsa's magic is quite the sight!
She flees through the night.

Learn Together With your child, make flash cards with simple one-syllable **rhyming words** (slow/flow, cat/hat, car/bar). Put one word on the front of each card and one or more rhyming words on the back.

More Fun with Rhymes

Anna chases after Elsa.

Finish the sentence with the rhyming word.

okay

Elsa feels like she has to run **away**.

Anna wants to tell her its _____ .

Rhyming words have letters at the end that sound the same.

(Circle) the words that rhyme.

Anna mounts her horse.

She goes after her sister of course.

Hans tells Anna to take care.

There is winter chill in the air.

Anna knows she has to go.

As she and her horse gallop through the snow.

Learn Together

Sing some favourite songs with your child, listening for rhymes in the lyrics.

39

Pictures Tell the Tale

From the picture, you can tell that Elsa is happy.
(Circle) the correct answer.

a. True   b. False

What do you think Elsa is doing?

_____

_____

What is something that makes you happy?

_____

_____

Learn Together With your child, examine and discuss this picture. What else does your child notice? When you read books together, encourage your child to use the picture clues to help them understand the story.

I Know How That Feels

Elsa is free.

She does not have to worry anymore.

She feels like she can be herself.

Elsa is not afraid to use her special powers.

What does this picture remind you of?

_____

_____

What makes you special?

_____

_____

Read the story to your child. Help your child **make connections** and respond to the questions. Ask your child to recall a time when they felt special. How did they feel?

Anna Gets Lost!

Anna's horse runs away.

She falls in the snow.

Her dress is frozen.

Anna is cold.

Anna sees a small building.

Anna goes to the building.

She wants to warm up by the fire.

Underline the clues in the story that help you answer these questions.

Is Anna warm or cold?

Where is Anna going?

Learn Together

With your child, describe what a favourite character from a book or movie looks like.

45

Beginning, Middle, ...

A story has a **beginning**.

Things happen in the **middle** of the story.

And then the story **ends**.

Read the story on pages 47 and 48.
Look for the **beginning**, **middle**, and **end**.

Anna goes inside Wandering Oaken's Trading Post and Sauna.

Anna buys supplies to climb the mountain.

Kristoff enters the Trading Post. He also buys supplies to climb the mountain. He is going to head north to find out why the storm is happening.

(To be continued)

Learn Together

Read the story to your child. Help them **make predictions** about what will happen next. They can use the picture and text to help them. Read the rest of this story on page 48.

... And End

(Continued from page 47)

Kristoff is rude to Oaken, the owner of Wandering Oaken's Trading Post and Sauna.

Kristoff says the prices are too high. He calls the owner a crook! The owner throws Kristoff out! Kristoff leaves with Sven. Anna follows Kristoff and Sven.

Learn Together

Read the story to your child, helping them identify the different parts of it. They can write **b** for the beginning, **m** for the middle (on page 47), and **e** for the end (on page 48). Talk about beginning, middle, and end when you read other stories.

Wolf Chase!

Put this story in order.

Number the boxes in the order the story happened.

Sven runs fast! He jumps over a huge canyon to escape from the wolves. They are safe.

Kristoff, Anna, and Sven start to go up the mountain.

Suddenly, they realize they are being chased by wolves!

Learn Together

Help your child figure out the story order. Find other pictures for your child to put in order. Encourage them to sequence other objects or actions.

What Do I Know?

Anna loves how beautiful winter can be.

Anna and Kristoff meet Olaf.

Olaf is a living snowman.

These sentences are facts.

They are part of a non-fiction text.

Winter is a chilly part of the year.
There are many activities to do in the winter.

You can build a snowman.

You can make snow angels.

You can have a snowball fight.

You can skate on ice.

You can go downhill skiing.

Underline two activities you like to do in the winter.

Learn Together

Read this **nonfiction text** to your child. Encourage your child's curiosity and questions as they read this and other nonfiction texts.

How Does That Feel?

Olaf loves the idea of summer.

Anna and Kristoff agree that summer would not be good for a snowman.

Here are some sentences describing summer.

This is a type of non-fiction text.

Summer days have blue skies.

The sun shines very bright.

The summer sun can feel hot on your skin.

People spend time on the beach.

They lay on the warm sand.

Underline the words that describe what the Summer looks like.

Circle a word that describes what the Summer feels like.

Elsa's Ice Palace

Olaf finds a stairway made of ice.

It leads to Elsa's ice palace.

"Whoa," says Anna as they reach the top.

The palace is amazing!

Elsa is not happy to see Anna.

She is afraid of hurting Anna with her icy powers.

What do you think will happen next?

_____

Read the passage to your child. Ask your child to **predict** what will happen next in the story.

57

Label It!

Labels give you information about what is in a picture.

What do the labels tell you about this picture?

winter hat

winter coat

rope

winter boots

Label this picture.

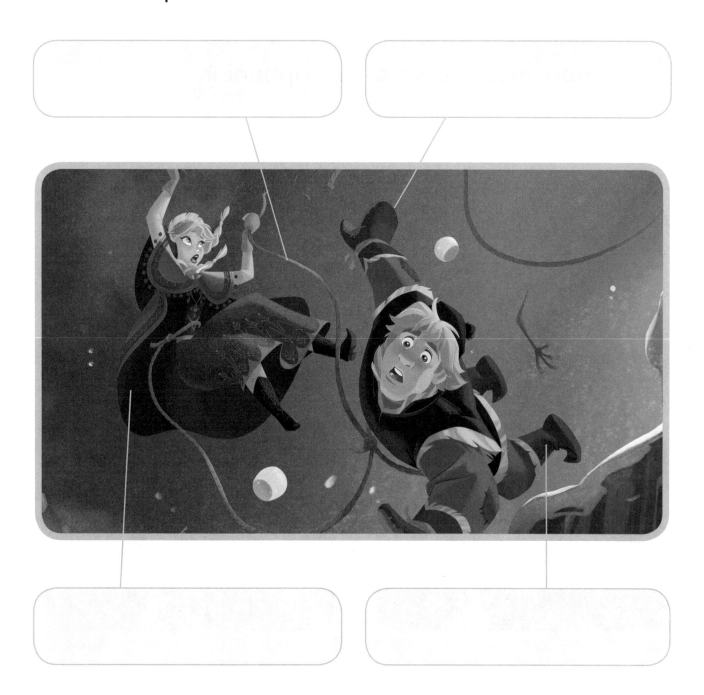

Learn Together Help your child label this picture, naming each object to label, sounding out the word, and helping them spell it. With your child, draw a picture of a neighbourhood park and label it.

Capture It with Captions

A **caption** tells you what is happening in a picture.

What do the captions tell you about these pictures?

The troll tells Anna how to thaw a frozen heart.

Anna's hair turns white!

Write a caption for the picture.

_____

Learn Together With your child, draw a picture. Discuss what is happening in it. Write a caption for the picture.

Lots of Sentences

A **sentence** tells you something.

A sentence can have different kinds of punctuation.

Hans is about to attack Elsa.

A sentence starts with a capital letter.

This sentence ends with a period.

Write a sentence about something you like to do. End the sentence with a period.

_____

_____

A sentence can ask a question.

A sentence can also show excitement.

Where is Olaf going?

> A question ends with a question mark.

Olaf loves to have fun!

> An exclamation mark shows excitement.

Write a sentence that asks a question.

_____

Write a sentence that shows excitement.

_____

Learn Together
Help your child write different sentences about your family. One sentence can end with a period, another with a question mark, and the third with an exclamation point.

Super Stories

A story has **characters**, a **setting**, and a **problem**.

Hans is about to attack Elsa.

Anna runs to her sister's side!

Anna reaches out to stop Han's sword.

Suddenly, her body turns to ice.

Han's sword shatters!

Elsa hugs Anna.

Anna starts to thaw!

An act of true love saves Anna's life!

Learn Together Help your child identify the setting, characters, and problem on page 65. Then help your child write a story about the picture. Discuss the characters, the setting, and the problem.

Dear ...

A letter is a note you write to be read by someone.

Elsa is happy see her sister.

Below is a letter she might write to her.

Dear Anna,

> Start your letter with a greeting.

Thank you for being by my side. I love you.

We will always have each other. I'm so glad we are home.

> A letter includes a message.

Love your sister,
Elsa

> Always sign your name.

Write a letter to someone special.

You can thank them for being kind.

_____

_____

_____

_____

_____

_____

_____

Learn Together

Help your child write their letter. Discuss what makes the person kind. Include those ideas in the letter. Create another copy of the letter, including a date. Mail the letter.

A Short Pause

A **comma** shows a short pause in a sentence.

Read these sentences out loud. Can you hear each pause?

This is a comma.

When Hans tries to hurt Elsa, Anna sends Hans flying with only one punch!

Finish the sentences.

Use a comma to show a pause.

First ○ _____

_____

Next ○ _____

_____

Then ○ _____

_____

Finally ○ _____

_____

Learn Together Help your child write a short story about their routine. Use commas to show pauses.

Short Stuff

A **contraction** is two words put together. An **apostrophe** replaces the missing letters.

This is an apostrophe.

I'm is a contraction that means **I am**.

<u>Underline</u> the words that have been put together in these sentences.

That's when Elsa realized love will bring back summer.

That is   That will   That have

It's a happy ending for the kingdom of Arendelle.

I have   It is   It will

Match these contractions with the words that have been put together.

it's   he is

we're   they are

he's   it is

they're   we are

Learn Together Look for other **contractions** as you read. Help your child read them and figure out what words have been put together.

1 to 10

Match the numbers
to the number word.

1		three
2		five
3		four
4		two
5		one

ten

      six

      nine

      seven

      eight

How many letters are in the name **Sven**?

Circle the correct number word.

four   **nine**   **five**

Learn Together

Your child can use modelling clay or pipe cleaners to form the numbers **1** to **10**.

73

11 and 12

Oaken has lanterns.

There are **11** lanterns.

Trace the number.

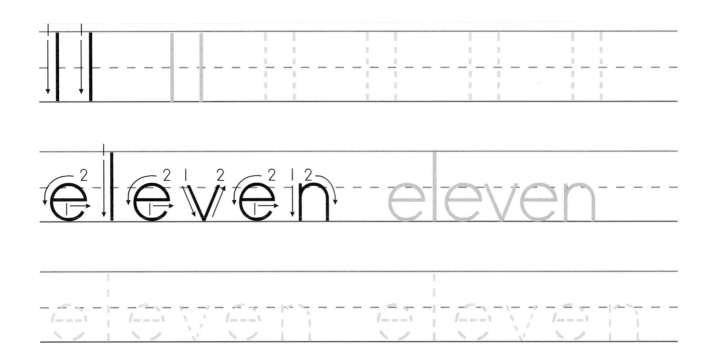

There are **12** shovels.

Trace the number.

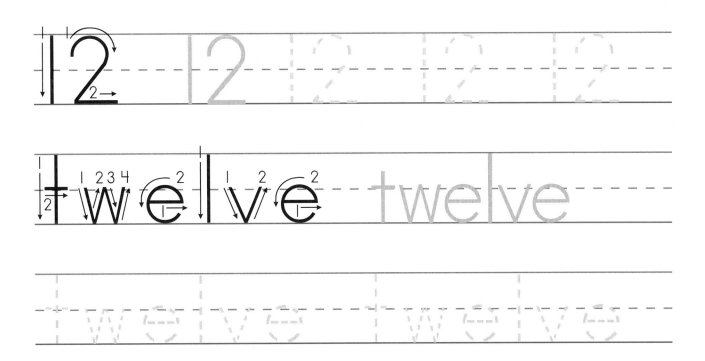

13 and 14

Elsa has **13**
colourful crystals.

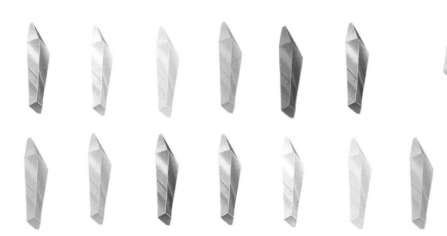

Trace the number.

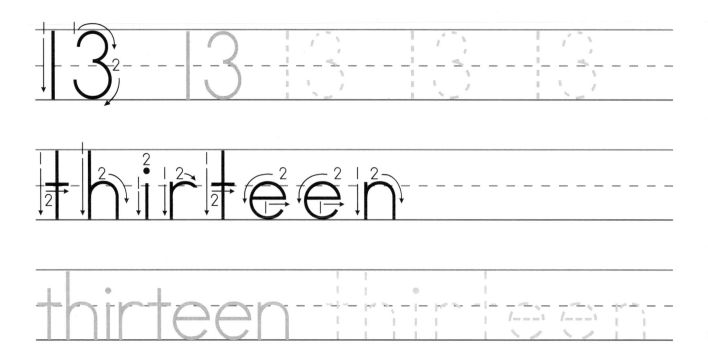

Now there are **14** colourful crystals.

Trace the number.

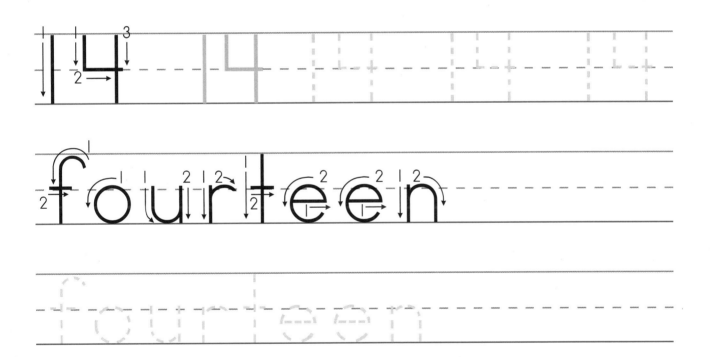

15 and 16

Olaf sees **15** kittens.

Trace the number.

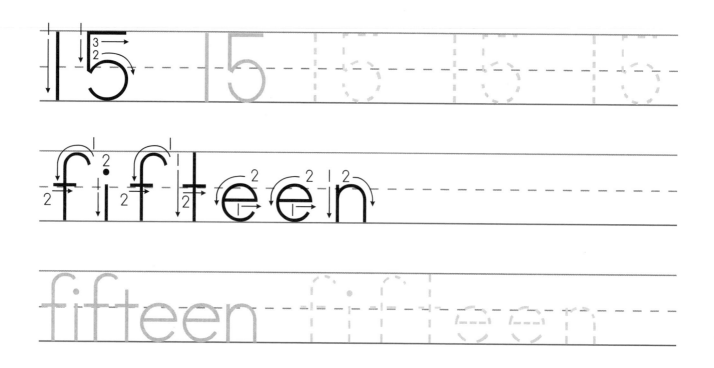

There are **16** balloons.

Trace the number.

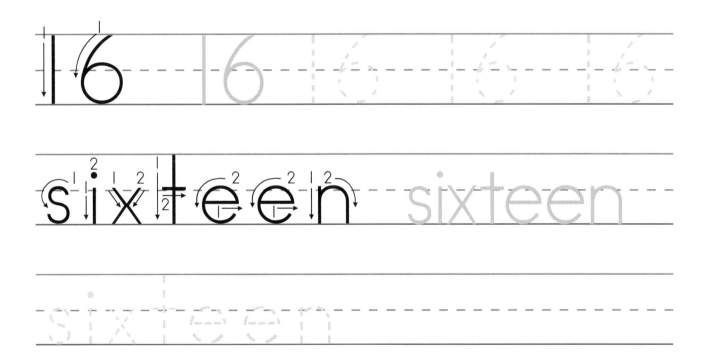

17 and 18

Draw **17** flowers.

Trace the number.

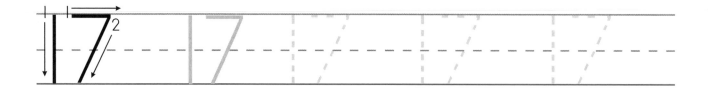

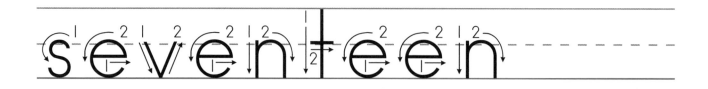

There are **18** ducklings.

Trace the number.

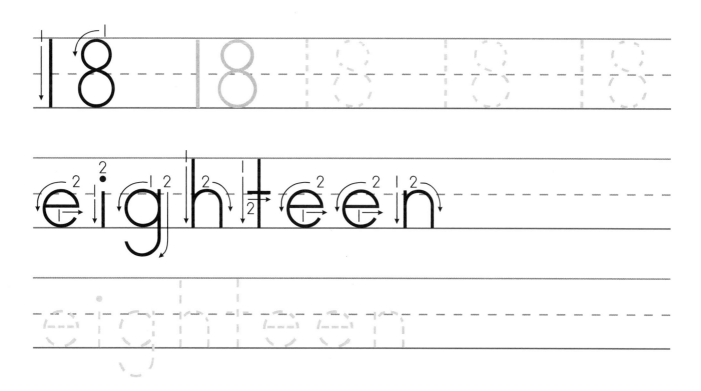

Discuss what your child notices about the numbers **10** through **19** (the number 1 before the second digit; the numbers are in the same order as the numbers 1 to 9). Connect this to their understanding of numbers and how they increase.

19 and 20

Olaf reads **19** books.

Trace the number.

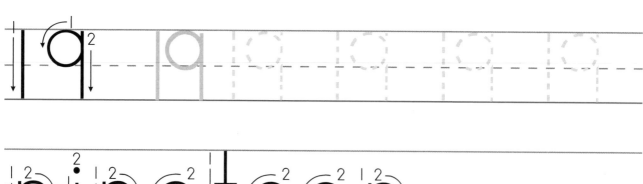

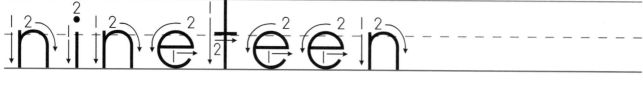

Now there are **20** books.

Trace the number.

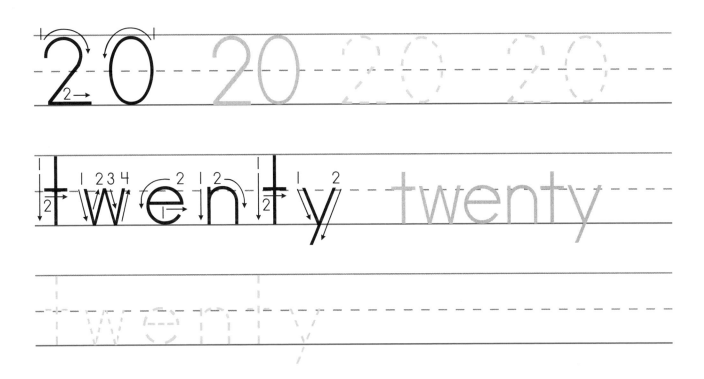

Learn Together With your child, take turns counting as you go up and down stairs in your home or in another building. Try to reach the number **20**.

Nothing at All

Sven has eaten all his carrots.

You can say this another way:

Sven has **zero** carrots left.

Zero or **0** is a number that represents nothing.

Trace the number.

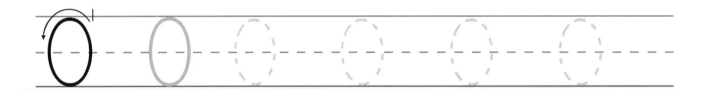

Print a **0** in the empty boxes

Learn Together Your child is just developing their understanding of zero. Provide them with opportunities to discuss how there are zero cookies left in the box or zero toys on the floor.

Story Time Number Lines

King Agnarr and Queen Iduna tell Anna and Elsa a bedtime story.

The story is about an enchanted forest full of magical spirits!

Anna and Elsa listen to the story.

On this number line, show how many candles King Agnarr is holding.

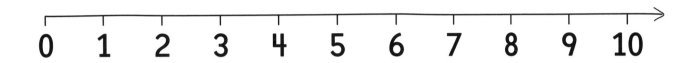

Show the number of children.

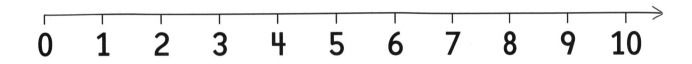

Show the number of people.

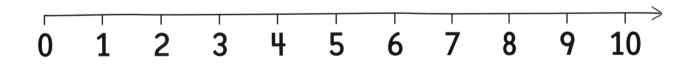

Learn Together

Help your child count by using the **number line**; as they count the items out loud they can shade the number line or place counters along it. Use these number lines to count other groups of objects in your home (blocks, stuffies, spoons).

One to One

Anna and Olaf are good friends.

Draw a line from Anna to Olaf.

Draw a picture of yourself and of a friend.

Draw a line from you to your friend.

Draw a line to match each picture on the left with a picture on the right.

Learn Together

Help your child identify other common examples of **one-to-one correspondence**. Match one bowl to one spoon or one mitten to its mate.

Count Them All!

Anna, Elsa, and their friends walk around Arendelle. There are many objects to see.

Count the objects in the group.

Trace each number below.

Draw that number of objects in the box.

Learn Together

With your child, collect groups of **11** to **20** objects (buttons, crayons, toy cars). Ask, "How many do you have?"

More or Fewer

Olaf reads more books.

Circle the group in each set that has **more** objects.

Count the objects in each group.

(Circle) the group in each set that has **fewer** objects.

Learn Together Divide **20** small objects into two groups (15 and 5; 4 and 16). Your child can count each group and say which has more objects. Which has fewer objects?

What's Missing?

Elsa hears a strange voice.

She does not know where it is coming from.

Can you solve the mystery?
Fill in the missing numbers.

4 5 _____

_____ 16 17

_____ 12 13

_____ 5 6

17 18 _____

9 10 _____

13 14 _____

15 16 _____

18 19 _____

_____ 11 12

10 11 _____

8 9 _____

7 8 _____

17 18 _____

16 17 _____

1 2 _____

Learn Together

Using **20** objects, make a group (7 crayons or 12 grapes). Your child can count them out loud. Add 1 more and ask how many there are now.

20 to 30

Trace the numbers.

20 20 20 20 20

21 21 21 21 21

22 22 22 22 22

23 23 23 23 23

24 24 24 24 24

25 25 25 25 25

Trace the numbers.

26   26   26   26

27   27   27   27

28   28   28   28

29   29   29   29

30   30   30   30

Learn Together

Printing the numbers **21** through **30** will probably be new to your child. Provide encouragement. Tell your child that knowing these numbers helps prepare them for Grade 2.

Sort It Out!

Elsa uses her magic, tossing snow into the air.

Images blossom from her fingertips.

Circle all the blue water elements.

Underline all the purple fire elements.

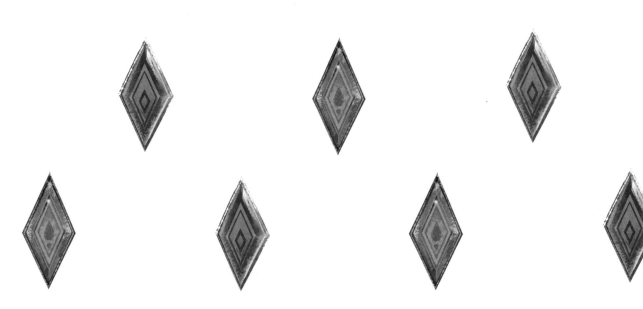

Draw something that belongs in each group.

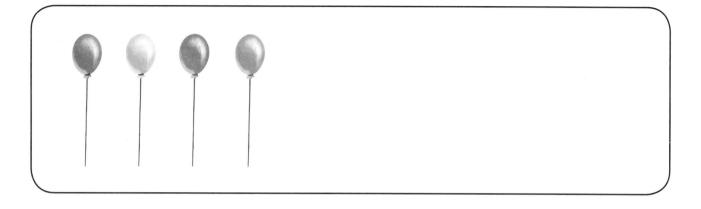

Learn Together Put a variety of socks on a table. Ask your child to help you decide how to sort them (by colour, size, or material).

What's the Pattern?

Elsa creates many small crystals that float in the air.

The crystals have patterns.

What comes next in each pattern?

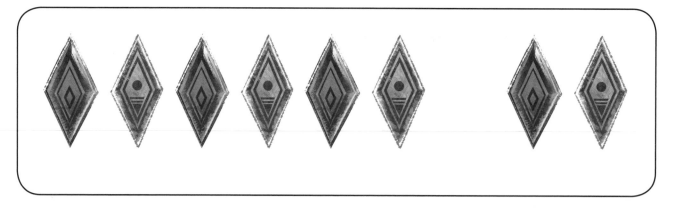

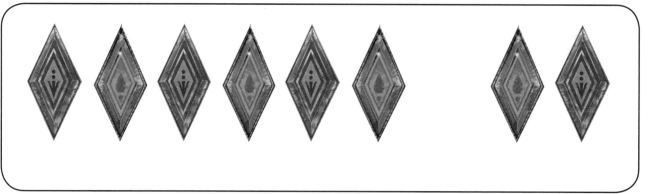

Look at these patterns.

What comes next in each pattern?

X Y X Y X _____

C C T C C _____

1 2 2 1 2 2 1 2 _____

3 3 4 3 3 4 3 _____

ABA ABA ABA _____

Learn Together

Talk about the patterns on these pages, describing each one. Your child can create a pattern using small items around your home (buttons, stickers). Ask your child to describe the pattern.

Making Patterns

There are lots of patterns.

Colour the objects below
to complete the pattern.

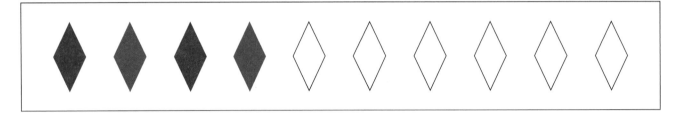

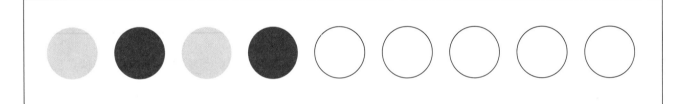

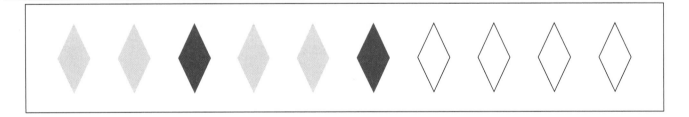

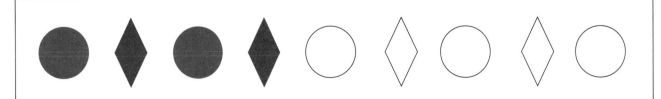

Choose **2** colours to make a pattern.

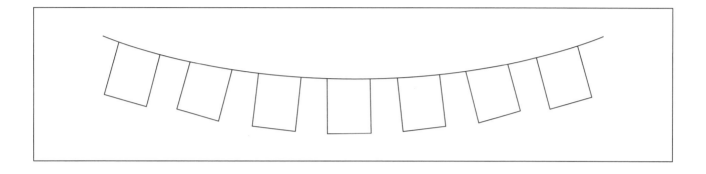

Choose **2** colours to make a pattern.

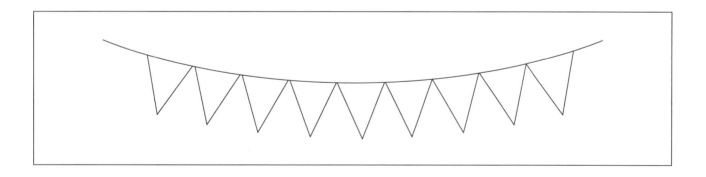

Learn Together

Talk about the patterns on these pages, describing each one. With your child, use small toy animals (or other toys) to make a pattern (horse, pig, horse, pig, horse, pig). Discuss the pattern's rules with your child (colour, size, animal type).

103

What's the Sum?

Sven is hungry

How many carrots will Sven eat?

This is another way to show the word **add**.

This is another way to show the word **equals**.

2   +   2   =   4

2 + 2 = 4 can also be written this way: 1 + 3 = 4

 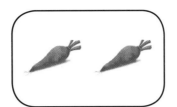

3 + 2 =

Show the sum another way.

The answer in an addition sentence is called the **sum**.

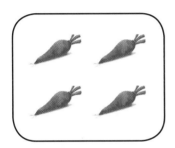 

4 + 4 =

Show the sum another way.

Count and Add

Elsa uses magic to make many elemental crystals.

Write the number in each group. Add the numbers together.

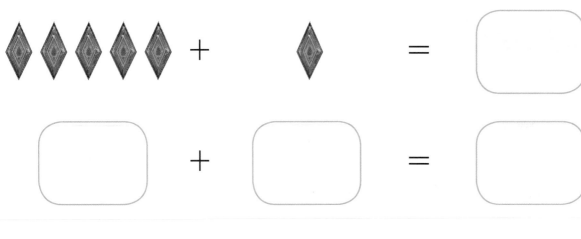

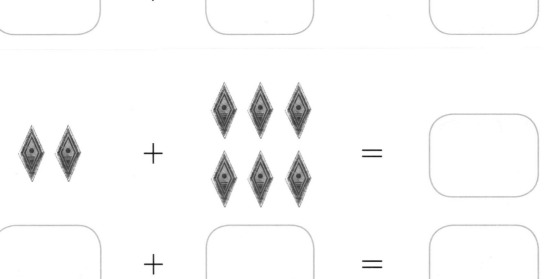

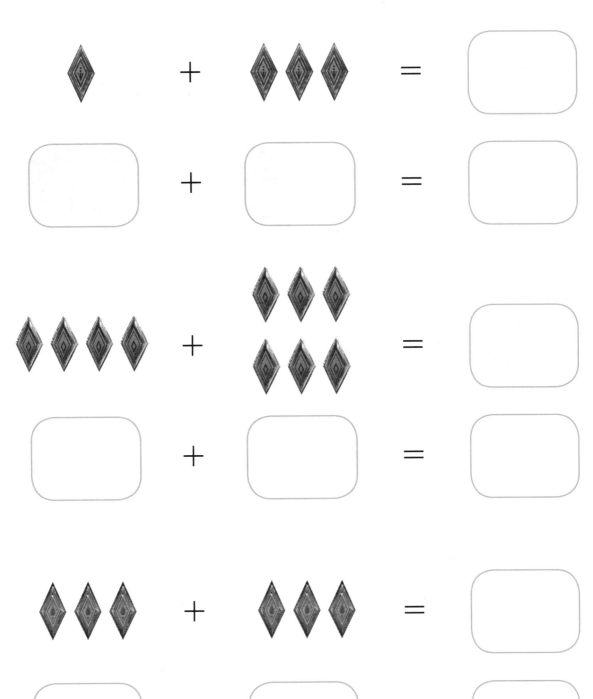

Add Them Up

The friends see many colourful leaves.

 + = ☐

☐ + ☐ = ☐

Show 2 + 5 on this 10-frame.

Show the sum another way.

108

Elsa and Anna are with their 3 friends.

Show 2 + 3 on this 10-frame.

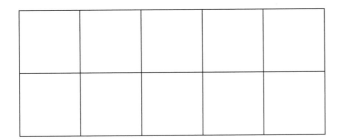

Show the sum another way.

Learn Together

With your child, you can make your own **10-frames**. These help children to interpret, build, and write addition (and subtraction) sentences.

Take It Away

Before

After

Olaf reads one of his books.

How many unread books does Olaf have?

| 7 | − | 1 | = | |

This is another way to show the word **subtract**.

The answer in a subtraction sentence is called the **difference**.

Before

After

 $-$  $=$

Before

After

 $-$ $=$

Learn Together

Help your child understand subtraction by using the language "take away" and by using objects (buttons, coins, blocks). Count the objects before and after taking some away from a group. You might also create a number line to help them subtract.

Take Away Some More

Olaf is separated from his friends.

Find the difference. Use the 10-frames or number line to help you.

4 − 1 =

5 − 2 =

5 − 3 =

9 − 7 =

12 − 2 = ☐

17 − 2 = ☐

18 − 8 = ☐

20 − 10 = ☐

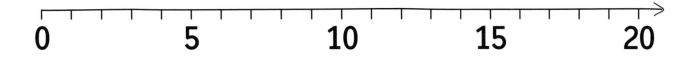

0   5   10   15   20

How Many Are Left?

The friends meet some soldiers from Arendelle in the enchanted forest.
Write the number of shields in each group.
Find the difference.

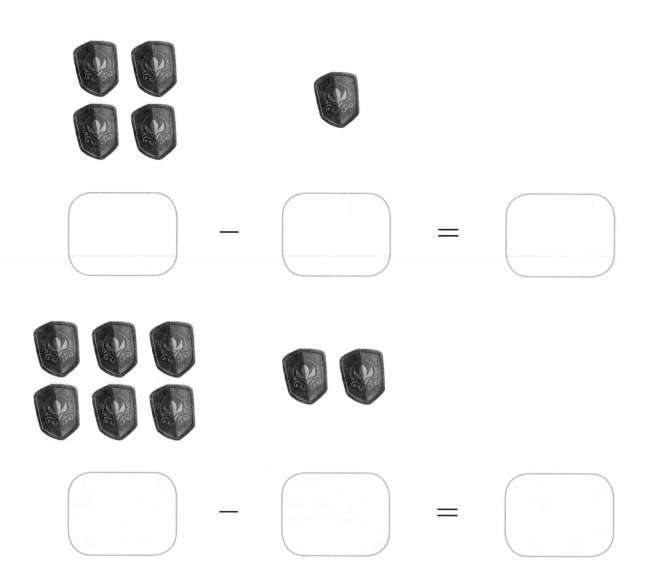

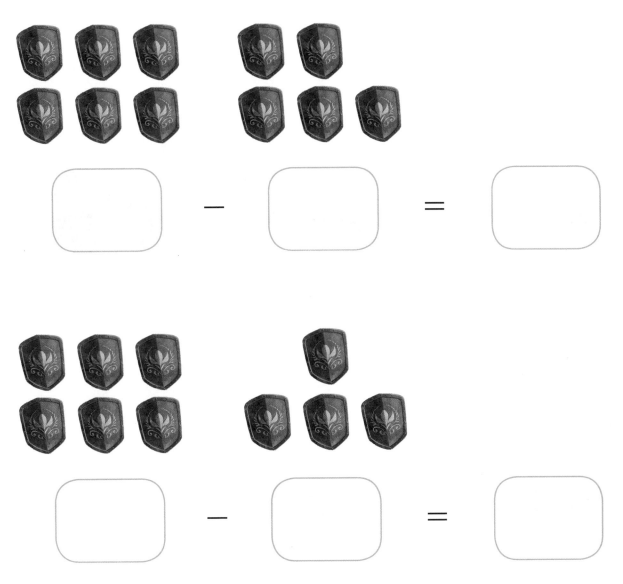

⬜ – ⬜ = ⬜

⬜ – ⬜ = ⬜

You can use a number line to help you.

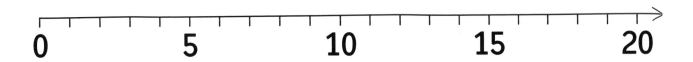

0   5   10   15   20

What's Left?

The friends travel
a long way. They pack
lots of things for their journey.

Count the objects in each group.

Find the difference.

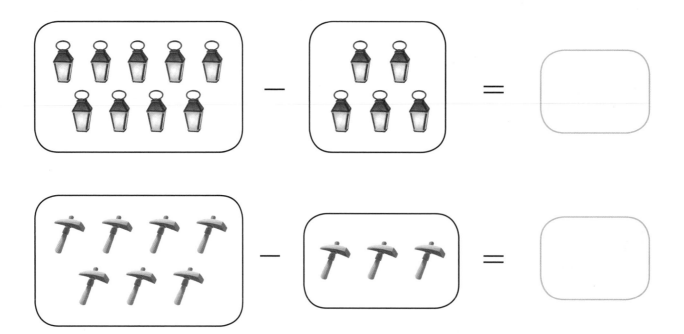

Solve these subtraction sentences.
Use the 10-frames to help you.

9 − 7 =

10 − 5 =   7 − 1 =

12 − 10 =   16 − 15 =

8 − 2 =   11 − 3 =

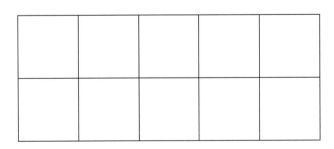

Learn Together

Your child can use counters and a
10-frame to help them solve each
subtraction sentence.

117

Add and Subtract

Tell an addition number story about this picture.

Write an addition sentence about your number story.

$$\boxed{} \quad + \quad \boxed{} \quad = \quad \boxed{}$$

Tell a subtraction number story about the picture.

Write a subtraction sentence about your number story.

$$\boxed{} \quad - \quad \boxed{} \quad = \quad \boxed{}$$

Solve these addition and subtraction sentences.
Use the 10-frames to help you.

12 + 3 =

17 − 2 =

12 − 10 =

11 + 1 =

2 + 15 =

19 − 15 =

15 − 3 =

14 + 2 =

Learn Together

Ask your child to tell you each number story. Help your child use small counters (beads, buttons) to solve each equation above.

How Long?

Kristoff plays the lute.
Instruments come
in different sizes.

How many blocks long are these instruments?

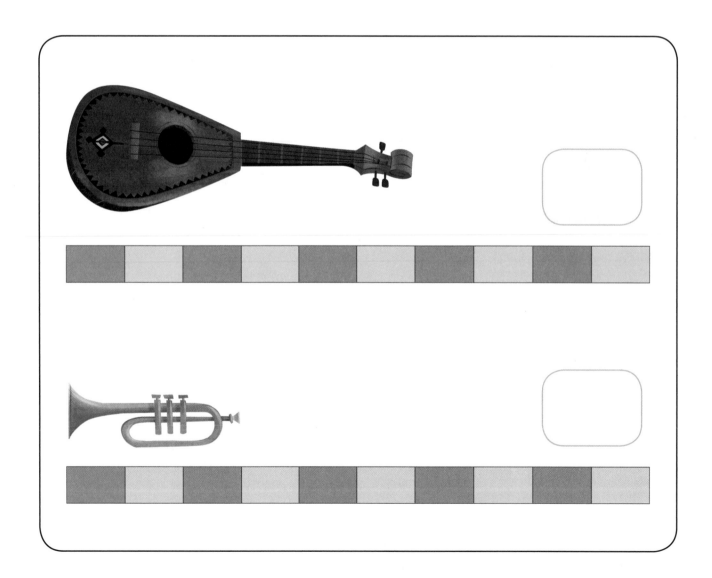

Draw an object that is 2 paper clips long.

Draw an object that is 3 paper clips long.

Draw an object that is 8 paper clips long.

Learn Together

Try measuring real objects around your home by using other **non-standard units** (straws, strips of paper of equal lengths, erasers).

Which Is Larger?

Kristoff is larger than his lute.

One size of each object is missing.

Draw the one that is missing.

Small   **Medium**   **Large**

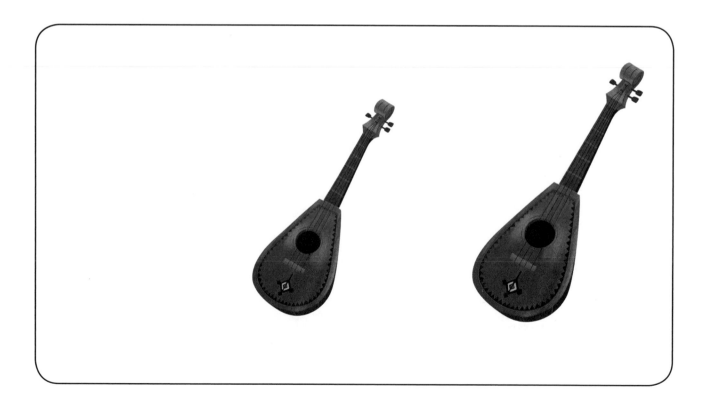

Small   Medium   Large

Small   Medium   Large

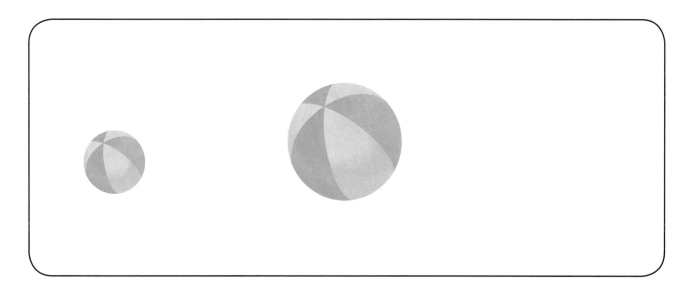

Learn Together   Help your child compare the size of various objects around the home. Encourage them to use the words *shorter*, *longer*, *larger*, and *smaller*.

123

Which Holds More?

Anna and Mattias hold bowls of steaming porridge. Both their bowls can hold the same amount of porridge.

(Circle) the bucket that holds the **most**.

$\left(\text{Circle}\right)$ the bucket that holds the **least**.

Learn Together As you bake or cook, ask your child to help you measure ingredients. Compare the tools you are using. ("Will this cup hold more than this spoon?")

Which One Is Heavier?

Which one is **heavier**?

(Circle) the one that is heavier.

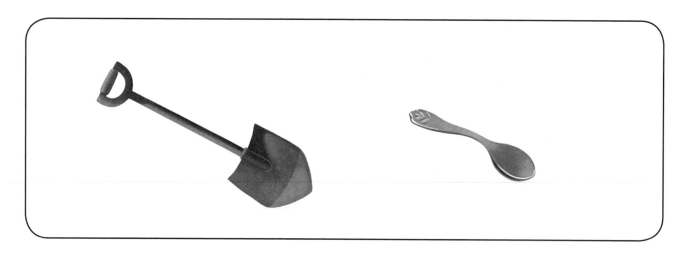

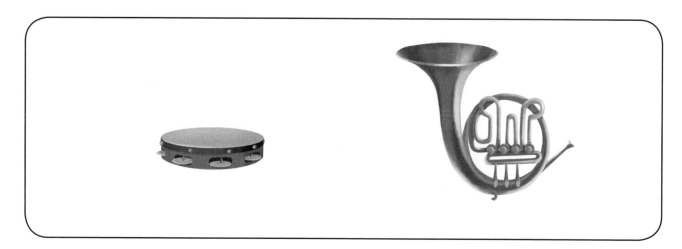

Draw something that is **light**.

Draw something that is **heavy**.

Learn Together

Gather some everyday objects that have very different masses. Your child can hold one item in each hand to determine which one has more mass.

Which One Is Lighter?

Anna can carry Olaf.

(Circle) the one in each box that is **lighter**.

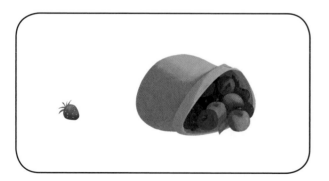

Draw an object on the left side of the teeter-totter.

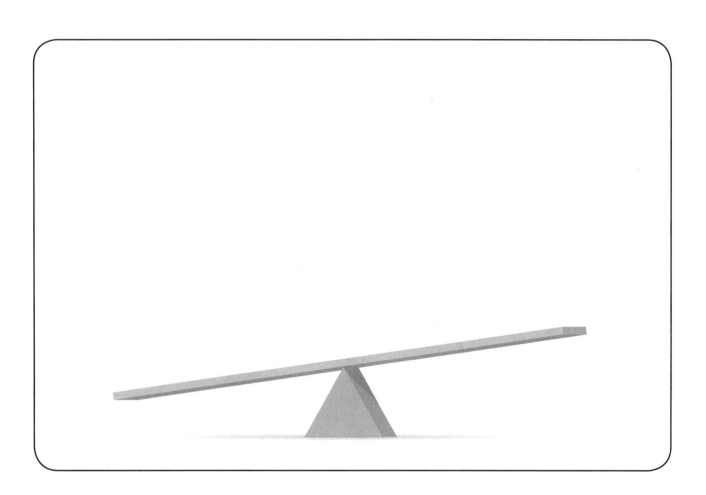

Draw something that is lighter on the right side.

Learn Together Ask your child to explain why they think one object might be lighter than another. Develop a theory that you can investigate together (larger objects are often heavier than smaller objects).

It's About Time!

We can measure time with a clock.

The little hand tells the **hour**.

The big hand tells the **minutes**.

Trace the numbers.

This clock reads ☐ o'clock.

Add the missing numbers.

What time is it? [ ] o'clock

Seeing Circles and Triangles

A **circle** is a perfectly round shape.

Put an ✖ on the circle.

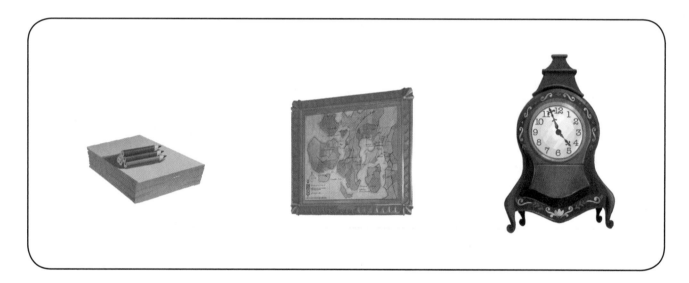

Cross out the shapes that are **not** circles.

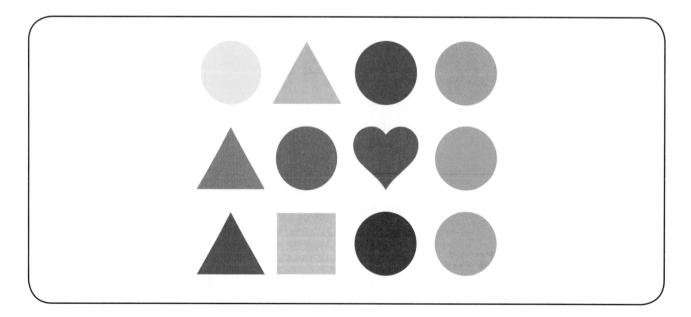

A **triangle** has three straight sides.

Put an ✖ on the triangle.

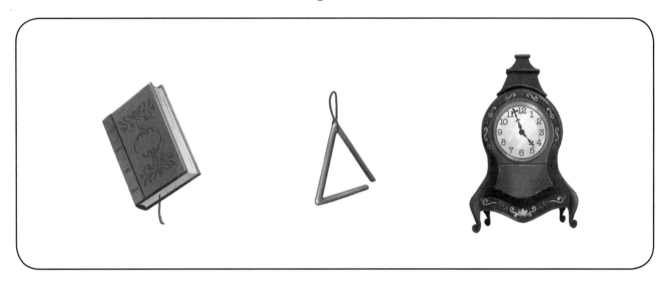

Cross out the shapes that are **not** triangles.

Learn Together

Discuss the characteristics of circles and triangles. Ask your child to identify circles and triangles in your home (circular logos on jars, triangular designs on boxes).

Looking for Rectangles and Squares

A **rectangle** has four sides.

Two sides are longer than the other two sides.

Circle the rectangles from the objects below.

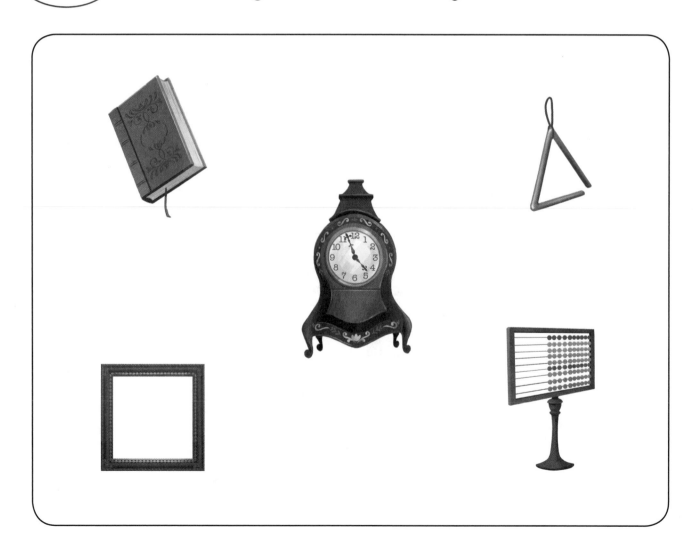

A **square** has four equal sides.

(Circle) the square from the objects below.

Write an **R** on the rectangles.

Write an **S** on the squares.

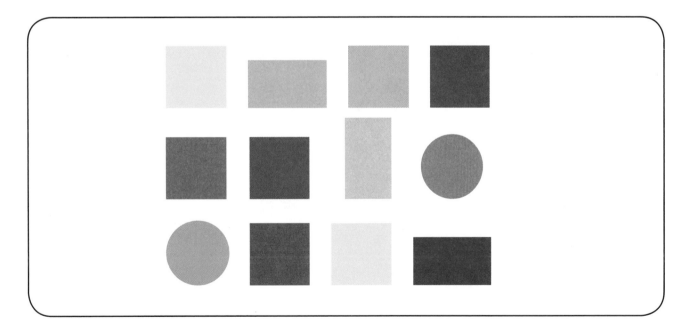

Solid Objects

The moon is a **sphere**.

Cross out the objects that are **not** spheres.

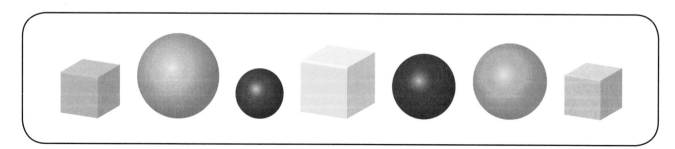

(Circle) the gifts that looks like a **cube**.

Cross out the objects that are **not** cubes.

Learn Together Find a sphere. With your child, describe it: "It looks like a ball. It rolls. It's round." Find a cube. With your child, describe it: "It looks like a box. It has 6 square sides. It has 8 corners."

137

Words for Where

Some words tell us where people or objects are.

Circle the words in each sentence that tells you where.

Olaf is **on top** of the books.

Sven is **behind** Kristoff.

Anna is **in front** of Elsa.

Look at this picture.

Circle something that is **above**.

Underline something that is **between**.

Learn Together

Your child can choose a word (beside, under) from these pages and act it out. Take turns acting and guessing.

Sort It!

Sven eats carrots and apples.

Draw 5 orange carrots in the first box.

Draw 5 red apples in the second box.

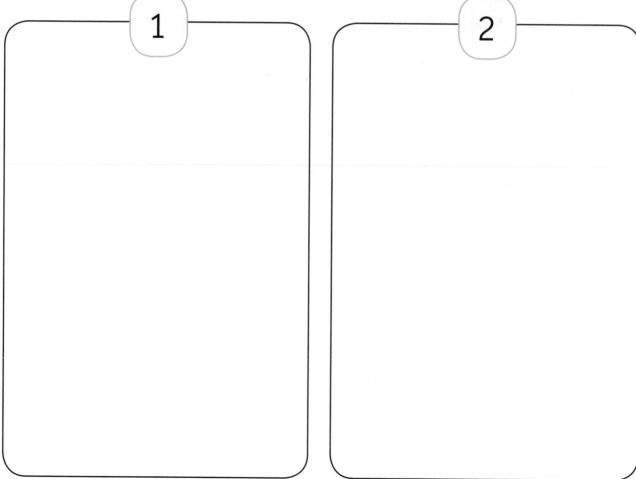

Olaf likes balloons and books.

Draw 5 red books in the first box.

Draw 5 blue balloons in the second box.

1

2

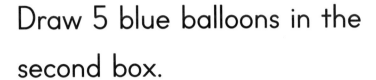

Learn Together Ask your child to collect a variety of toys (blocks, cars, dolls). Discuss how they might be sorted (by material, colour, or whether or not your child likes them).

The Book Graph

Olaf loves to read books.

Olaf's Books

This **picture graph** is one way to show how many books Olaf has read.

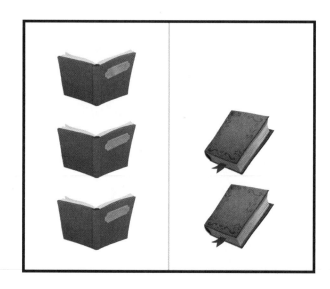

read   unread

How many books did Olaf read?

How many books are unread?

Create your own picture graph.

Label your picture graph.

Give it a title.

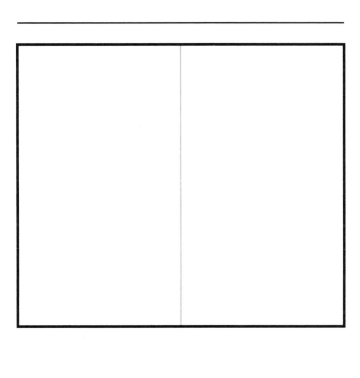

Tell one thing your picture graph shows.

Help your child create their **picture graph**. To keep it manageable, guide them to choose objects that they don't have too many of and that they can sort into two categories. For example, they could sort their shoes; the sorting rule might be laces or no laces.

Show How Many

Look at all the balloons Olaf has!

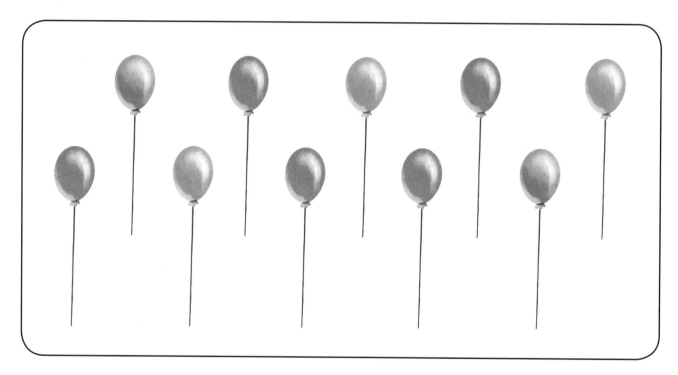

Create a picture graph.

Olaf's Balloons

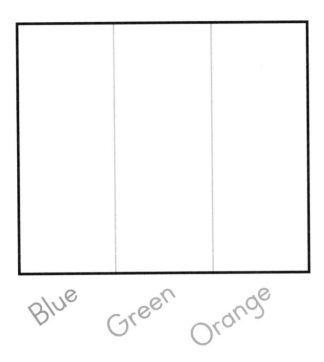

Blue   Green   Orange

What colour balloon does Olaf have the most of? _____

What colour balloon does Olaf have the least of? _____

What's Next?

After your child has completed the topics in this book, you can complete some of the following activities together.

Letter Recognition

- Read alphabet books together. Encourage your child to suggest other words that begin with each letter.

- Serve a bowl of alphabet soup or cereal. Challenge your child to identify every letter and then connect each letter to an object in your home (*c* is for *couch*).

- Every week, choose a new letter to be a "super" letter. Print the letter extra big, and place it where your child can see it. Challenge your child to find as many objects as possible that begin with that letter.

- Help your child create a dance or song for each letter of the alphabet.

- Stamp out letter shapes in the snow or sand.

- Give your child various materials (pencils, crayons, markers, clay, beads, sand, chalk, paper, magnet letters) that they can use to make letters and words.

Word Knowledge

- Ask your child to help you create a grocery list.

- Your child can read familiar words on boxes and cans of food.

- Your child can read signs in your neighbourhood.

- Pause as you read to your child, allowing them to read sight words or other words they know.

- As you read together help your child look for homophones. Discuss how the words sound the same but are spelled differently (your/you're, to/two/too). Your child may recognize a few common homophones as they read but may still use the wrong homophone.

Comprehension

- Invite your child to tell you stories about their day.

- Encourage your child to make connections to stories they read and shows they watch.

- Your child's knowledge of the world can help them as they read; as they read stories, they connect to that knowledge to help them make sense of the text. So, for example, if you are reading them a story about a sport they like, they will find it easier to understand new information and words in the text.

- Tell stories together. Get your child to finish a familiar story.

- Your child can retell simple or familiar stories they have heard; this is an important step in understanding how stories are structured.

- As you read or watch shows, ask your child questions to help them make predictions.

- Encourage your child's questions about stories and nonfiction text.

- Point to the pictures in stories. Talk about the characters or setting.

- Tell a familiar story out of sequence and ask your child to fix it.

- Talk about the beginning, middle, and end of stories.

Writing

- Create sentence starters for your child to finish. ("I want a _____." "Do you want to go to the _____?" "I love _____.")

- Create a digital photo album together, with photos of your child's life. Help them write the captions.

- Write stories (lists, letters, poems, texts) with your child.

- Write notes to each other and leave them in secret places.

- Together, create a treasure map for your child to follow.

- Your child can write labels or captions for their drawings.

What's Next?

- Count together as you do everyday activities. ("How many toys are we putting away?" "How many blocks does this house need? Let's count!")

- Sing counting songs or skipping rhymes with your child.

- Read counting books together.

- Practise counting by starting at numbers between 11 and 20. This sequence is harder for children to remember because it's irregular.

- Make a counting book using your child's toys and digital photos.

- Give your child various materials (pencils, crayons, markers, clay, beads, sand, chalk, paper) that they can use to make numbers and number words.

- Place 1 to 20 small objects, such as dried beans, into a cup. Your child can estimate and then count the number of objects.

- Use 10 small objects to make number groups (6 objects, 5 objects). Your child can write the number and the word for that number.

Patterns

- Invite your child to help you sort as you do chores (putting away dishes, laundry, or toys).

- Look for patterns in your home and neighbourhood.

- Take photos of patterns you see. With your child, create a digital pattern book with captions to describe each pattern.

- Use stickers or toys to create patterns for each other to complete.

Addition and Subtraction

- Add or subtract as you do everyday activities together. ("How many more apples do we need in the bag to make 10?" "We have too many carrots for the stew. We only need 5. How many should we take away?")

- Play card and board games that involve adding or subtracting.

- Create clues for a scavenger hunt that can be solved only by simple addition or subtraction. ("You need to find 2 toys in your room and 3 toys in the living room. How many toys will you have then? That answer will tell you how many steps to take from the bathroom to your room to find the next clue.")

Measurement

- Read and follow recipes together. Allow your child to measure ingredients and identify how much of something is needed. ("This soup needs 3 onions and 1 carrot.")

- Count the squares in the sidewalk as you walk in your neighbourhood. How many squares is your home from the park?

- Experiment with the mass and capacity of everyday objects. ("Do you think this book is heavier than this pencil? Why do you think that? Let's lift them both to find out." "Do you think this cup will hold more water than this bowl? How can we find out?")

Geometry

- Look for shapes as you walk in your neighbourhood. ("That door is a rectangle. The window is a square.")

- Take photos of the shapes you see and create a shapes photo album.

- Look for 3-D objects in your home, noting which objects are which shapes (cans are cylinders). Your child can use a notebook to draw and label the objects and shapes they found.

Collecting and Using Data

- Encourage your child to sort objects, such as toys, by providing them with bins or other containers. Talk about the rules they use to sort. ("All of the red toys went in the red bin. Are you sorting by colour?")

- Help your child develop a survey for family members to complete. ("What movie should we watch tonight?" "What toppings should we have on our pizza?") Work together to graph the results.

- Look for graphs, tables, and charts as you read nonfiction. Help your child understand the information in these texts.

Glossary

addition sentences: number sentences or equations used to express addition. For example, $4 + 1 = 5$.

alphabetical order: to arrange words according to the order of letters in the alphabet; your child is at a stage where they can arrange a couple of words in alphabetical order by first letter only (that is, *bread, clock, dog*, but not *brake, bread, break*).

contractions: words created by joining two words and using an apostrophe to replace the missing letters (*don't, I'm, you're*). Your child is ready to read simple and common contractions but will have greater difficulty with uncommon ones and may not be ready to spell or write any contractions.

estimating: to use understanding of numbers to make an educated guess at an answer to a problem. At this stage, your child is ready to estimate how many objects are in a group of 10.

letter combinations: two or more consonants that work together in a word, but each consonant can be distinctly heard. For example, the *sn* in *snake* or the *ft* in *raft*. Your child will also be using *digraphs*. Digraphs are two consonants working together to make one sound. For example, the *sh* in *shake* or the *ck* in *block*.

long vowel sound: the sound a vowel makes depends on the letters around it and its position in the word. An example of a long vowel sound is the sound *a* makes in *cake* (as opposed to the short vowel sound of the *a* in *cat*).

make connections: a reading strategy that supports your child's understanding of texts. There are three types of connections (text to self, text to text, and text to world). At this stage of development, your child will mostly be making text-to-self connections; that is, as they listen to you read, they will make connections to those things they have experienced or feelings they have had. Meaningful connections can help them understand what a character is feeling or what has happened in the text.

make predictions: to make educated guesses about what will happen next. Your child is ready to make predictions when they look at pictures or hear the title of a book. They are also ready, while reading, to use clues in the text and pictures to make an educated guess about what will happen next.

nonfiction text: writing based in truth or reality; nonfiction texts include posters, instructions, diagrams, diaries, some magazine and newspaper articles, blogs, and so on. Your child is beginning to identify the differences between fiction and nonfiction.

non-standard units: units for measuring that are not conventional. So, for example, your child might measure two books by using an eraser ("This book is 6 erasers long. That book is 8 erasers long."). While your child may not be ready to understand centimetres, litres, kilograms, etc., they can use non-standard units to measure.

number line: a line showing numbers placed in order. Number lines can help your child as they add or subtract or think about how one number is related to another (3 comes before 6, 10 is 9 numbers away from 1).

number stories: one or more statements that illustrate math equations. For example, the equation $2 + 2 = 4$ could be told as a story about two children who are joined by two friends.

one-to-one correspondence: in math, the idea that objects in one group correspond to objects in a second group. Understanding this concept helps your child form a sound foundation for understanding math.

ordinal numbers: numbers that express order, such as *first, second, third.*

pictograph: a graph that uses pictures or symbols to represent objects. Your child will be creating a variety of graphs in school, including vertical and horizontal pictographs, bar graphs, and line plots.

rhyming words: words that have the same end sound (*pop, stop, hop*). Your child is ready to identify rhyming words and the part of the word that makes the same sound. As you list rhyming words together, try to focus on those that have the same spelling (*feed* and *seed*, rather than *feed* and *bead*).

short vowel sound: the sound a vowel makes depends on the letters around it and its position in the word. An example of a short vowel sound is the sound *a* makes in *hat* (as opposed to the long vowel sound of the *a* in *hate*).

sight words: also called *popcorn words* or *high-frequency words*; these are the short, simple words your child will begin to recognize immediately as they become more familiar with reading. Sight words for children at this level include a, about, am, an, and, are, as, be, because, big, but, by, did, do, don't, for, from, had, has, have, he, her, here, him, his, how, I, if, I'm, in, into, is, it, just, like, me, mother, my, no, not, now, of, on, one, or, our, out, over, see, she, so, the, their, them, then, there, they, this, to, too, two, up, us, was, we, went, were, what, when, where, who, you, your.

subtraction sentences: number sentences or equations used to express subtraction. For example, $6 - 2 = 4$.

10-frames: two-by-five rectangle frames into which counters are placed to illustrate numbers less than or equal to 10. These frames help teach counting and can help your child with addition and subtraction.

word families: a group of words related in some way, such as beginning or ending with the same sound (*bed, fed, red* are part of the *ed* word family; *black, blue, blond* are part of the *bl* word family).

Answers

Let's Create a Wintry Alphabet

Elsa fills the castle with snow for Anna.
Fill in the missing letters.

A B C **D** E F **G** H I J K L M N
O P Q **R** S T U **V** W X Y Z

6

Fill in the missing letters.

a b c **d** e f **g** h i j **k** l m n
o p **q** r **s** t u v **w** x y **z**

7

Elsa wants to protect her sister.
Trace the letters.

Elsa keeps her
powers a secret
from Anna.

21

Let's Make Words

These words are all part of the
ay word family.
Trace the first letter.
Say each word out loud.

hay   **d**ay   **w**ay   **p**lay

These words are all part of the an word family.
Trace the first letter.
Say each word out loud.

can   **p**an   **r**an   **m**an

22

Anna wants to play with Elsa. Trace the missing letters.

Can you come to
build a snowman?
Let's go play!

23

Fill in the missing popcorn words.
Today is Elsa's coronation. **s h e** is nervous
to open the castle gates.
Anna is excited to have guests in the castle! She
can not wait to meet **t h e m**.

25

Underline the popcorn words below.
Anna is excited to see all of Arendelle.
Anna wants to look at the whole town!
She meets Hans. He makes her smile.
Anna is very happy!

27

Read these popcorn words out loud

because   with   that
       very   some

Fill in the missing popcorn words.
All the people are **v e r y** excited to see
Elsa, **b e c a u s e** they have never
seen their queen.
Anna eats **s o m e** chocolate at the party.

29

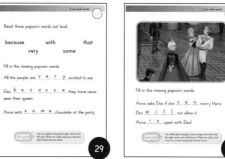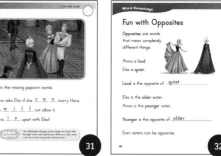

Fill in the missing popcorn words.
Anna asks Elsa if she **c a n** marry Hans.
Elsa **w i l l** not allow it.
Anna **i s** upset with Elsa!

31

Fun with Opposites

Opposites are words
that mean completely
different things.

Anna is loud.
Elsa is quiet.

Loud is the opposite of **quiet**

Elsa is the older sister.
Anna is the younger sister.

Younger is the opposite of **older**

Even sisters can be opposites.

32

Match each word to its opposite.

old ——— bad
slow ——— hot
good ——— new
tall ——— short
cold ——— fast

33

Match each word to its opposite.

right ——— night
day ——— out
in ——— wrong
dark ——— dirty
clean ——— light

35

Rhyme Time

Rhyming words have letters at the end
that sound the same.
(Circle) the words that rhyme.

ice   nice   dice   snow   glow   blow
cold   gold   old

Say the words out loud. Listen to the rhyme.

36

(Circle) the words that rhyme.

Anna and Hans want to marry with Elsa's permission.
"No" is Elsa's final decision.

Elsa tells Anna, "It's not true love."
Anna is upset and accidentally removes Elsa's glove.

Elsa's magic is quite the sight!
She flees through the night.

37

More Fun with Rhymes

Anna chases after Elsa.
Finish the sentence with the rhyming word.

okay

Elsa feels like she has to run away.
Anna wants to tell her its **okay**

38

Rhyming words have letters at the end
that sound the same.
(Circle) the words that rhyme.

Anna mounts her horse.
She goes after her sister of course.

Hans tells Anna to take care.
There is winter chill in the air.

Anna knows she has to go.
As she and her horse gallop through the snow.

39

41 — From the picture, you can tell that Elsa is happy.
(Circle) the correct answer.
a. True b. False
What do you think Elsa is doing?
Answers may vary.
What is something that makes you happy?
Answers may vary.

43 — Elsa is free.
She does not have to worry anymore.
She feels like she can be herself.
Elsa is not afraid to use her special powers.
What does this picture remind you of?
Answers may vary.
What makes you special?
Answers may vary.

45 — Anna's horse runs away.
She falls in the snow.
Her dress is frozen.
Anna is cold.
Anna sees a small building.
Anna goes to the building.
She wants to warm up by the fire.
Underline the clues in the story that help you answer these questions.
Is Anna warm or cold?
Where is Anna going?

50 — Comprehension

Wolf Chase!

Put this story in order.
Number the boxes in the order the story happened.

3

Sven runs fast! He jumps over a huge canyon to escape from the wolves. They are safe.

51

1 — Kristoff, Anna, and Sven start to go up the mountain.

2 — Suddenly, they realize they are being chased by wolves!

53 — These sentences are facts.
They are part of a non-fiction text.
Winter is a chilly part of the year.
There are many activities to do in the winter. Answers may vary.
You can build a snowman.
You can make snow angels.
You can have a snowball fight.
You can skate on ice.
You can go downhill skiing.
Underline two activities you like to do in the winter.

55 — Here are some sentences describing summer.
This is a type of non-fiction text.
Summer days have blue skies.
The sun shines very bright.
The summer sun can feel hot on your skin.
People spend time on the beach.
They lay on the warm sand.
Underline the words that describe what the Summer looks like.
(Circle) a word that describes what the Summer feels like.

57 — Olaf finds a stairway made of ice.
It leads to Elsa's ice palace.
"Whoa," says Anna as they reach the top.
The palace is amazing!
Elsa is not happy to see Anna.
She is afraid of hurting Anna with her icy powers.
What do you think will happen next?
Answers may vary.

59 — Label this picture.
Rope   Glove/Mitten
Cape   Boot

61 — Write a caption for the picture.
Kristoff and Anna are riding Sven.

62 — Writing

Lots of Sentences

A sentence tells you something.
A sentence can have different kinds of punctuation.
Hans is about to attack Elsa.
A sentence starts with a capital letter.   This sentence ends with a period.
Write a sentence about something you like to do.
End the sentence with a period.
I like to go skating.

63 — A sentence can ask a question.
A sentence can also show excitement.
Where is Olaf going?   A question ends with a question mark.
Olaf loves to have fun!   An exclamation mark shows excitement.
Write a sentence that asks a question.
Do you want to go skating?
Write a sentence that shows excitement.
Skating is so much fun!

70 — Writing

Short Stuff

A contraction is two words put together. An apostrophe replaces the missing letters.
This is an apostrophe.
I'm is a contraction that means I am.
Underline the words that have been put together in these sentences.
That's when Elsa realized love will bring back summer.
That is   That will   That have
It's a happy ending for the kingdom of Arendelle.
I have   It is   It will

71 — Match these contractions with the words that have been put together.
it's — he is
we're — they are
he's — it is
they're — we are

72 — Number Sense

1 to 10

Match the numbers to the number word.
1   three
2   five
3   four
4   two
5   one

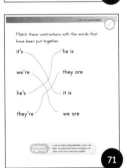

73
6   ten
7   six
8   nine
9   seven
10   eight
How many letters are in the name Sven?
Circle the correct number word.
four   nine   five

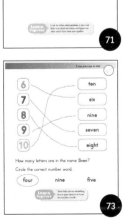

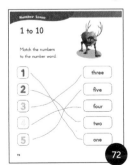

Answers

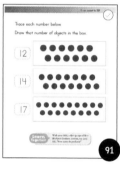

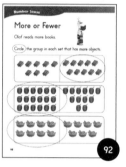

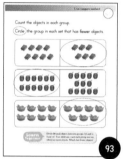

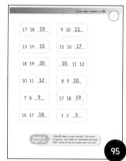

Sort It Out!

Elsa uses her magic, tossing snow into the air. Images blossom from her fingertips.

Circle all the blue water elements.

Underline all purple fire elements.

98

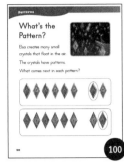

What's the Pattern?

Elsa creates many small crystals that float in the air. The crystals have patterns. What comes next in each pattern?

100

Look at these patterns. What comes next in each pattern?

X Y X Y X Y

C C T C C T

1 2 2 1 2 2 1 2 2

3 3 4 3 3 4 3 3

ABA ABA ABA A

101

Making Patterns

There are lots of patterns. Colour the objects below to complete the pattern.

102

3 + 2 = 5

Show the sum another way.

The answer in an addition sentence is called the sum.

4 + 4 = 8

Show the sum another way.

105

Count and Add

Elsa uses magic to make many elemental crystals. Write the number in each group. Add the numbers together.

+ = 6

5 + 1 = 6

+ = 8

2 + 6 = 8

106

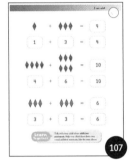

+ = 4

1 + 3 = 4

+ = 10

4 + 6 = 10

+ = 6

3 + 3 = 6

107

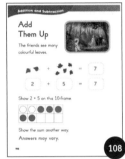

Add Them Up

The friends see many colourful leaves.

+ = 7

2 + 5 = 7

Show 2 + 5 on this 10-frame.

Show the sum another way. Answers may vary.

108

Elsa and Anna are with their 3 friends.

+ = 5

2 + 3 = 5

Show 2 + 3 on this 10-frame.

Show the sum another way.

Answers may vary.

109

Take It Away

Before   After

Olaf reads one of his books. How many unread books does Olaf have?

7 - 1 = 6

This is another way to show the word subtract.

The answer in a subtraction sentence is called the difference.

110

155

Answers

Before   **After**

$7 - 3 = 4$

Before   **After**

$12 - 5 = 7$

111

Addition and Subtraction

Take Away Some More

Olaf is separated from his friends.

Find the difference.

Use the 10-frames or number line to help you.

$4 - 1 = 3$

$5 - 2 = 3$

$5 - 3 = 2$

$9 - 7 = 2$

112

$12 - 2 = 10$

$17 - 2 = 15$

$18 - 8 = 10$

$20 - 10 = 10$

0   5   10   15   20

113

Addition and Subtraction

How Many Are Left?

The friends meet some soldiers from Arendelle in the enchanted forest.

Write the number of shields in each group.

Find the difference.

$4 - 1 = 3$

$6 - 2 = 4$

114

$6 - 5 = 1$

$6 - 4 = 2$

You can use a number line to help you.

0   5   10   15   20

115

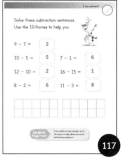

Addition and Subtraction

What's Left?

The friends travel a long way. They pack lots of things for their journey.

Count the objects in each group.

Find the difference.

$ - = 4$

$ - = 4$

116

Solve these subtraction sentences. Use the 10-frames to help you.

$9 - 7 = 2$

$10 - 5 = 5$ $7 - 1 = 6$

$12 - 10 = 2$ $16 - 15 = 1$

$8 - 2 = 6$ $11 - 3 = 8$

117

Addition and Subtraction

Add and Subtract

Tell an addition number story about this picture.

Write an addition sentence about your number story.

$4 + 5 = 9$

Tell a subtraction number story about the picture.

Write a subtraction sentence about your number story.

$9 - 5 = 4$

118

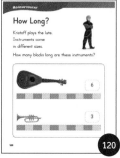

Solve these addition and subtraction sentences. Use the 10-frames to help you.

$12 + 3 = 15$ $2 + 15 = 17$

$17 - 2 = 15$ $19 - 15 = 4$

$12 - 10 = 2$ $15 - 3 = 12$

$11 + 1 = 12$ $14 + 2 = 16$

119

Measurement

How Long?

Kristoff plays the lute. Instruments come in different sizes.

How many blocks long are these instruments?

6

3

120

156

Which Holds More?

Anna and Mattias hold bowls of steaming porridge. Both their bowls can hold the same amount of porridge.

(Circle) the bucket that holds most.

124

I can compare capacity

(Circle) the bucket that holds least.

125

Which One Is Heavier?

Which one is heavier?
(Circle) the one that is heavier.

126

Which One Is Lighter?

Anna can carry Olaf.
(Circle) the one in each box that is lighter.

128

It's About Time!

We can measure time with a clock.
The little hand tells the hour.
The big hand tells the minutes.
Trace the numbers.

This clock reads 5 o'clock.

130

Add the missing numbers.

What time is it? 10 o'clock

131

Seeing Circles and Triangles

A circle is a perfectly round shape.
Put an ✗ on the circle.

Cross out the shapes that are not circles.

132

I can identify shapes

A triangle has three straight sides.
Put an ✗ on the triangle.

Cross out the shapes that are not triangles.

133

Looking for Rectangles and Squares

A rectangle has four sides.
Two sides are longer than the other two sides.
(Circle) the rectangles from the objects below.

134

I can identify shapes

A square has four equal sides.
(Circle) the square from the objects below.

Write an R on the rectangles.
Write an S on the squares.

S R S
S S R
S S R

135

Answers

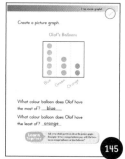

Congratulations

to

_____

for completing this workbook!

Keep up the amazing work!